11+ Verbal Reasoning

For the **CEM** test

It's no secret that the CEM 11+ test can be seriously tricky. But don't worry — this CGP Practice Book will give children a brilliant head start on their test preparation.

In the first few sections, they can practise answering questions on one topic at a time. Then, when they're ready for more realistic 11+ practice, give the Assessment Tests a try.

It's all set at just the right level for ages 8-9, so it's perfect for building their confidence. And with detailed answers included in a pull-out booklet, marking is a breeze!

How to access your free Online Edition

This book includes a free Online Edition to read on your PC, Mac or tablet. You'll just need to go to **cgpbooks.co.uk/extras** and enter this code:

2437 7001 8656 3222

By the way, this code only works for one person. If somebody else has used this book before you, they might have already claimed the Online Edition.

Practice Book – Ages 8-9

with Assessment Tests

How to use this Practice Book

This book is divided into two parts — themed question practice and assessment tests.
There are answers with detailed explanations in the pull-out answer book.

Themed question practice

- Each page has practice questions on a different theme. Use these pages to work out your child's strengths and the areas they find tricky. The questions get harder down each page.

- Your child can use the smiley face tick boxes to evaluate how confident they feel with each topic.

Assessment tests

- The second half of the book contains eight assessment tests, each with a mix of question types from the first half of the book.

- You can print off multiple choice answer sheets from cgpbooks.co.uk/11plus/answer-sheets, so your child can practise taking the tests as if they're sitting the real thing.

- Use the printable answer sheets if you want your child to do each test more than once.

- If you want to give your child timed practice, give them a time limit of 20 minutes for each test, and ask them to work as quickly and carefully as they can.

- The tests get harder from 1-8, so don't be surprised if your child finds the later ones more tricky.

- Your child should aim for a mark of around 85% (36 questions correct) in each test. If they score less than this, use their results to work out the areas they need more practice on.

- If they haven't managed to finish the test in time, they need to work on increasing their speed, whereas if they have made a lot of mistakes, they need to work more carefully.

- Keep track of your child's scores using the progress chart on the inside back cover of the book.

- This book gives your child intensive practice of the Verbal Reasoning sections of the test. There will be other elements on the real 11+ test, such as Maths and Non-Verbal Reasoning.

- Although our question types are based on those set by CEM, we cannot guarantee that your child's actual 11+ exam will take the same format or contain the same question types as this book.

Published by CGP
Editors: Claire Boulter, Lucy Loveluck

Contributors: Chloe Buckley, Lucy Towle, Paul Warnes

With thanks to Holly Poynton and Janet Berkeley for the proofreading.

Please note that CGP is not associated with CEM in any way.
This book does not include any official questions and it is not endorsed by CEM.

ISBN: 978 1 78908 169 5

Printed by Elanders Ltd, Newcastle upon Tyne
Clipart from Corel®

Based on the classic CGP style created by Richard Parsons.

Contents

Plurals

Plurals

Underline the correct plural from the brackets to complete the sentence. Look at this example:

> We keep the sharp (knifes **knives**) in the top drawer.

1. Two famous (**chefs** cheves) arrived to judge the cooking competition.

2. We'll divide the cupcake into two (halfs **halves**).

3. The officers' (wifes **wives**) were invited to watch the parade.

4. The (**shelves** shelfs) in the bakery are full of bread.

5. The prize money was divided and stored in two separate (**safes** saves).

6. Many people feel strongly about their (believes **beliefs**).

7. I enjoy learning about the (lifes **lives**) of kings and queens.

/7

Plurals

Write the correct plural of the word in brackets. Look at this example:

> We played with all the ____toys____ (**toy**).

8. I believe in _____ (**fairy**) because I saw one in the garden.

9. All the _____ (**turkey**) escaped through the open gate.

10. My uncle built two more _____ (**chimney**) on his roof.

11. There were _____ (**fly**) on the compost heap.

Hint: Words which end in a consonant and 'y' take an 'ies' plural ending.

12. Playing the trombone is one of my _____ (**hobby**).

13. The _____ (**pony**) are running happily around the field.

/7

14. _____ (**Daisy**) are my favourite flower.

Homophones

Underline the correct homophone from the brackets to complete each sentence. Look at this example:

> I can't (**fined** **find**) my red shoes.

1. I'll (**grate** great) some cheese for the pizza.

2. When you go to Paris, can I come (**too** to) ?

Hint: Homophones are words that sound the same but mean different things.

3. My granny used to work as a (**maid** made) at the royal palace.

4. We're going to (there **their**) holiday caravan by the sea.

5. Have you (scene **seen**) the new Wilkinson Brothers film?

6. I promised that I (wood **would**) lend her my blow-up crocodile.

7. I've found the perfect place to (**bury** berry) my treasure.

7 /7

Underline the correct homophone from the brackets to complete each sentence. Look at this example:

> I (**paced** paste) around the room while I brushed my teeth.

8. He hurled the stone right (through **threw**) the open window.

9. After my morning ride, I had a (horse **hoarse**) throat.

10. There were a hundred people in the (**queue** cue) for the snooker match.

11. The carpet had to be sent back because there was a (**flaw** floor) in it.

12. The farmer stood under the tree while the (yew **ewe**) fed her lamb.

13. No noise is (aloud **allowed**) in the library.

/7

14. My dad was (**banned** band) from the school music competition.

Prefixes and Suffixes

Prefixes

Underline the word with the correct prefix from the brackets to complete each sentence. Look at this example:

The garage was an (**independent**   **imdependent**) business.

1. Another word for naughty is (**disobedient**   **unobedient**).

2. Sally was so tired that she was (**incapable**   **uncapable**) of eating her soup.

3. The tiny crack in the statue made it (**nonperfect**   **imperfect**).

4. Natalie had a particular (**dislike**   **unlike**) for chocolate.

5. The teacher said that the (**misuse**   **nonuse**) of fireworks would be dangerous.

6. Kayla can be (**unpolite**   **impolite**) if she's not on her best behaviour.

7. I was (**unable**   **disable**) to see over the head of the man in front.

/7

Suffixes

Add the suffix **ity**, **ion** or **ous** to the word in brackets to complete the sentence. Look at this example:

Chi is the best gymnast because she has good __flexibility__ (**flexible**).

8. Gethin only likes watching _____ (**act**) films.

9. Iftikar sold his stamp _____ (**collect**) at the fair.

Hint: You might need to change the spelling of the word slightly when you add the suffix.

10. Sameera noticed the _____ (**similar**) between the sisters.

11. The boys were very _____ (**adventure**) in the woods.

12. Robert did not pick the toadstool in case it was _____ (**poison**).

13. My dad uses a satellite _____ (**navigate**) system to find his way.

14. I went canoeing at the outdoor _____ (**active**) centre.

/7

Section One — Spelling and Grammar

Awkward Spellings

Vowels

For each sentence, add a vowel to spell the word correctly.
Look at this example:

> The eleph_a_nt lived in a big field in the safari park.

1. My brother has started his own comp____ny selling gadgets.

2. The cars were produced in the new fact____ry.

3. My little brother was miser____ble when it rained.

4. My mum's friend won £100 on the lott____ry.

5. Gran gave me a wildlife calend____r for my birthday.

6. I'll try to d____scribe what I saw as accurately as I can.

7. Will you defin____tely have enough time?

Hint: Vowels are the letters 'a', 'e', 'i', 'o' and 'u'.

6 / 7

Consonants

Underline the correct word from the brackets to complete each sentence. Look at this example:

> The dog (**wagged**   **waged**) his tail eighty times a minute.

8. He (**waded**   **wadded**) into the river to catch the fish.

9. I (**triped**   **tripped**) over and fell into the swimming pool.

10. Naomi had run out of (**wraping**   **wrapping**) paper, so she used newspaper.

11. Carlos couldn't believe he had been (**chossen**   **chosen**) for the squash team.

12. Marina knew she'd been (**robed**   **robbed**) when she noticed her purse was missing.

13. Gail was (**riding**   **ridding**) her scooter when she found the abandoned car.

14. Antonio is (**thiner**   **thinner**) than the last time I saw him.

7 / 7

Section One — Spelling and Grammar

Mixed Spelling Questions

> Underline the correct word from the brackets to complete each sentence. Look at this example:
>
> Her (**father** farther) likes to be called Papa.

1. I was so (inpatient **impatient**) that I couldn't sit still.

2. Frank seemed to wear a (differant **different**) wig every day.

3. Nobody (nose **knows**) where the bunch of flowers came from.

4. The kangaroo didn't pick up on the (**tension** tention) in the room.

5. (Leafs **Leaves**) turn orange and red in the autumn.

6. Mr Herbert is going to take us to pick (blackberrys **blackberries**).

7. Juliet had (**written** writen) her notes, but they had disappeared.

8. My mum said I could go out if I helped her wash the (dishs **dishes**).

9. If you lead an (**inactive** unactive) life, you may put on weight.

10. Shen started doing (voluntry **voluntary**) work when he lost his job.

11. There were lots of (**stories** storys) in Dad's book of fairy tales.

12. The mayor (**pinned** pined) a gold sticker on the winning entry.

13. I followed the (**pattern** patern), but somehow I made a shirt with three sleeves.

14. The library was packed with (referance **reference**) books.

15. When we were in the jungle, we had to (**purify** purefy) our water.

Mixed Spelling Questions

Each sentence contains a spelling mistake. Underline the word with the error and write the correct spelling on the line. Look at this example:

Lilly is <u>completley</u> hopeless in the morning. _____*completely*_____

1. What are you smileing about? _____

2. I missread the instructions and glued my eye shut. _____

3. The parachute landed at the foot of the cliffes. _____

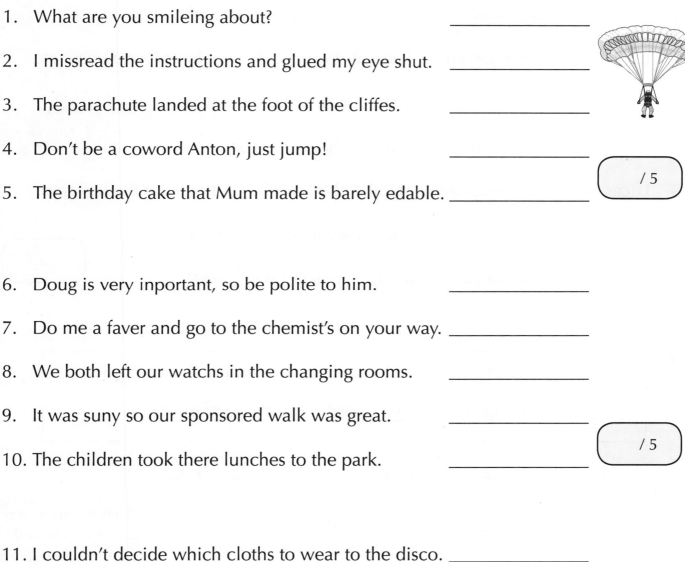

4. Don't be a coword Anton, just jump! _____

5. The birthday cake that Mum made is barely edable. _____

/ 5

6. Doug is very inportant, so be polite to him. _____

7. Do me a faver and go to the chemist's on your way. _____

8. We both left our watchs in the changing rooms. _____

9. It was suny so our sponsored walk was great. _____

10. The children took there lunches to the park. _____

/ 5

11. I couldn't decide which cloths to wear to the disco. _____

12. The king was the most powerfull man in the land. _____

13. George was running laps around the boundry. _____

14. This yoghurt has no flavour: it's totally tastless. _____

15. The bees were huming loudly inside the hive. _____

/ 5

Verbs

Underline the correct verb from the brackets to complete each sentence. Look at this example:

> Kristin **(play <u>played</u> playing)** golf yesterday.

1. Ana **(sang sing sings)** beautifully in the concert last night.

2. If Chelsea had **(know knew known)** the way, she would not have been late.

3. When I got home, I **(eat ate eaten)** a delicious sandwich.

4. Last Sunday I **(rode ride ridden)** my bike to the park.

5. Lucas was **(kept keep keeping)** the class goldfish at home for the holidays.

6. Geraint **(choose chose chosen)** a lolly at the sweet shop.

/ 7

7. Michelle **(began begun begin)** her breakfast with cereal.

Write the verb in brackets in the past tense. Look at this example:

> Mo **(give)** ___gave___ Katie a birthday present.

8. Minna ran away as the dog **(race)** _____ towards her.

9. Wen **(find)** _____ his shoe in the dustbin.

10. Fin **(bring)** _____ his colouring pencils to the art class.

> Hint: Some words are irregular and several letters may change when they change tense.

11. Henry **(take)** _____ the bus to work on Wednesday.

12. Paula had **(buy)** _____ the cake for the party.

13. Mary **(speak)** _____ quietly to the little puppy.

/ 7

14. Gary **(think)** _____ that the Brussels sprouts tasted awful.

Adverbs and Conjunctions

Adverbs

Underline the best adverb from the brackets to complete each sentence. Look at this example:

> The baby yawned **(<u>sleepily</u> fiercely)** in its cot.

1. The men danced **(wisely gracefully)** across the stage.

2. Rivers often flow more **(kindly swiftly)** after heavy rain.

3. The fishermen sang **(instantly cheerfully)** all the way home.

4. Leopards are **(closely slowly)** related to lions.

5. The whole class **(obediently badly)** followed the teacher out of the door.

6. Sina marched **(boldly endlessly)** to the cave to face the dragon.

7. The chocolate sauce smelt **(consistently faintly)** of garlic.

Hint: Think about what both answers mean and choose the one that fits the sentence best.

/ 7

Conjunctions

Underline the best conjunction from the brackets to complete each sentence. Look at this example:

> James sang well, **(<u>but</u> unless)** Abhik sang beautifully.

8. I read the book quickly **(because or)** I wanted to know what would happen.

9. Kieran washed the car **(unless but)** he forgot to mow the lawn.

10. I'm going swimming **(but so)** I have bought new goggles.

11. I think cats are interesting, **(although until)** I definitely prefer rabbits.

12. Niamh added the butter **(nor before)** Aadi added the jam.

13. Katherine had to walk quickly **(or while)** she would be left behind.

14. You should always sing **(because while)** you bake bread.

/ 7

Section One — Spelling and Grammar

Mixed Grammar Questions

Each sentence has one grammatical error. Underline the word which is wrong and write the correct word on the line. Look at this example:

Rachel is <u>make</u> bread.   <u>making</u>

1. Yesterday, Mia waters the flowers.   _____

2. When I'm older, I wanted to be a doctor.   _____

3. I make my bed careful every day.   _____

4. Simon is look forward to his trip to London.   _____

5. We was pleased with the ending to the story.   _____

6. Did you found the keys that you had lost?   _____

7. He never remembers to packed toothpaste.   _____

/ 7

Underline the word in each sentence which matches the part of speech in brackets. Look at this example:

I was afraid to play the antique <u>piano</u>. **(noun)**

8. When the orange ball rolled towards the river, Callum chased after it. **(adjective)**

9. When I left the caravan, I could hear someone talking loudly. **(adverb)**

10. Are you really going to run a marathon? **(noun)**

11. The dog ruined my favourite jumper. **(adjective)**

12. The diamond ring sparkled in the sunlight. **(verb)**

> Hint: If you can't remember what 'verbs', 'adjectives', 'nouns' or 'adverbs' are, have a look at the glossary in the back of the book.

13. Lucia had been waiting patiently for fifteen minutes. **(adverb)**

/ 7

14. The cat was tired after his performance. **(adjective)**

Odd One Out

Four of the words in each list are linked. Underline the word that is **not** related to the other four. Look at this example:

cow   hen   sheep   pig   <u>monkey</u>

1. robin   crow   wren   hamster   sparrow

2. cloudy   morning   windy   raining   sunny

3. lawn   flowerbed   sofa   patio   shed

4. lord   princess   king   duke   prince

5. car   ship   lorry   van   bus

Hint: If you're stuck, try to picture all the objects in your head and think about what they have in common.

/ 5

6. potato   banana   carrot   parsnip   turnip

7. pile   heap   line   stack   mound

8. bed   oven   kettle   microwave   fridge

9. wool   needle   thread   yarn   string

10. shorts   jumper   trousers   skirt   leggings

/ 5

11. gold   ruby   emerald   sapphire   diamond

12. boot   bonnet   exhaust   wheel   driver

13. clock   second   minute   hour   day

14. chalet   flat   bungalow   office   cottage

15. blonde   ginger   coral   brunette   auburn

/ 5

Closest Meaning

Underline the word that means the same, or nearly the same, as the word on the left. Look at this example:

fast   <u>rapid</u>   slow   chase   fly

1. **afraid**   brave   spooky   fearful   precise

2. **laugh**   happy   sob   rumble   chuckle

3. **bite**   meal   nibble   tooth   take

4. **sweet**   sour   chocolate   sugary   tasty

5. **dirty**   messy   wet   filthy   tidy

/ 5

6. **lucky**   rich   fortunate   happy   winner

7. **brave**   strong   angry   confident   heroic

8. **hold**   pull   catch   grasp   take

9. **allow**   deny   confess   agree   permit

10. **lively**   active   angry   energy   happy

/ 5

11. **cunning**   clever   sly   thoughtful   stupid

12. **spare**   over   enough   provide   extra

13. **cramped**   crowded   gathered   busy   plenty

14. **same**   similar   alike   identical   related

15. **complete**   end   whole   part   perfect

> Hint: Think about what the word in bold means before you look at the options.

/ 5

Closest Meaning

Complete the word on the right so that it means the same, or nearly the same, as the word on the left. Look at this example:

foe e n e m y

1. **wide** b r _ _ d

2. **uneven** b u _ _ y

3. **walk** _ t r _ l l

4. **tiny** _ m a _ l

5. **powerful** s _ r _ n g

> Hint: Make sure you consider all possible meanings of the word on the left to help you think of the right answer.

/ 5

6. **create** _ a k _

7. **intelligent** c _ e _ e r

8. **sociable** f _ i _ d l y

9. **discover** _ i n _

10. **grumble** m _ _ n

/ 5

11. **relaxed** c a _ _

12. **unclear** b l u _ _ d

13. **beautiful** _ r e t _ _

14. **bend** f _ _ d

15. **organised** p _ _ _ a r e d

/ 5

Section Two — Word Meanings

Opposite Meaning

Underline the word that means the opposite, or nearly the opposite, of the word on the left. Look at this example:

ill   nice   <u>well</u>   sick   happy

1. **shiny**   dull   smooth   bumpy   clear

2. **sharp**   edged   blunt   pointed   flat

3. **kind**   type   happy   angry   cruel

4. **dislike**   hate   love   give   please

5. **smooth**   even   cracked   seamless   rough

/ 5

6. **hollow**   thick   heavy   solid   weighed

7. **boring**   pleasing   happy   busy   interesting

8. **success**   failure   prize   loss   mistake

9. **adore**   admire   annoy   despise   ignore

10. **distinct**   clear   heavy   faint   puzzling

/ 5

11. **follow**   lead   force   ahead   obey

12. **fragile**   sturdy   breakable   dainty   heavy

13. **flexible**   bendy   stiff   hard   tough

14. **major**   young   useless   lazy   unimportant

15. **fresh**   old   faded   dry   stale

Hint: Don't get Opposite Meaning and Closest Meaning questions confused — read the instructions carefully before you start.

/ 5

Section Two — Word Meanings

Opposite Meaning

Complete the word on the right so that it means the opposite,
or nearly the opposite, of the word on the left. Look at this example:

strong   w e a k

1. **dim**   b r i ☐ ☐ t

2. **alive**   d ☐ ☐ d

3. **hard**   ☐ o f ☐

4. **fix**   b r ☐ ☐ k

5. **loose**   t i ☐ ☐ t

Hint: If you can't think of the answer, use the letters that you've been given to help you think of words which would fit.

/ 5

6. **loud**   ☐ u ☐ ☐ t

7. **tall**   s ☐ ☐ r ☐

8. **neat**   ☐ n t i ☐ y

9. **hidden**   e x ☐ ☐ s e d

10. **shrink**   g ☐ ☐ w

/ 5

11. **listen**   s ☐ ☐ a k

12. **add**   r ☐ ☐ o v e

13. **argue**   a ☐ r e ☐

14. **fine**   t h ☐ ☐ k

15. **elderly** ☐ ☐ u n ☐

/ 5

Reorder Words to Make a Sentence

Rearrange the words so that each sentence makes sense. Underline the word which doesn't fit into the sentence. Look at this example:

> I have to <u>lamp</u> room my tidy

The remaining words can be arranged into the sentence:
I have to tidy my room.

1. was yesterday present birthday my

2. I my open yo-yo with played

3. are mud wellingtons pies my favourite

4. dad has a hair moustache my huge

5. giant I put the killed

/ 5

6. my lunchbox went forgot I

7. my not really grapes likes hamster

8. the blew tree down sun in gale the

9. my a bird's looked like rain hair nest

/ 5

10. I worms night enjoy eating

11. quite school was today books fun

> Hint: If you get stuck, try writing the sentence out in a different order to see what makes sense.

12. favourite colour my soft green is

13. I clocks forward close to put the forgot

14. we project Egypt a pyramid on did

15. tadpole my grown pond has pet legs

/ 5

Related Words

The words in capitals are related in some way. Choose the word from the brackets that fits best with the words in capitals.
Look at this example:

CAR BUS FERRY COACH   (road drive <u>train</u> cargo journey)

Hint: The answer probably won't be a word that describes the first four words — it's more likely to be another example of something of the same type.

1. PINK GREEN ORANGE BLUE (yellow bright primary colour hue)

2. BAG SUITCASE SATCHEL HOLDALL (wallet bowl pocket rucksack things)

3. EAGLE WREN WOODPECKER SPARROW (bird tree fly worm pigeon)

4. SON MOTHER UNCLE COUSIN (relative family daughter boy child)

5. BOOT CLOG TRAINER SLIPPER (foot sole laces shoe sandal)   / 5

6. SNOW HAIL RAIN SLEET (fog sun cloud drizzle wind)

7. LION TIGER JAGUAR COUGAR (hippo cheetah cat animal striped)

8. ORGANISE ORDER SORT ARRANGE (tidy neat clean folder type)

9. TERRIER CORGIE COLLIE SPANIEL (dog poodle wolf puppy pet)

10. BOIL STEAM ROAST BAKE (hot fry oven burn dinner)   / 5

11. SCULPT DRAW PHOTOGRAPH SKETCH (pen art paint write sing)

12. CUBE CYLINDER PRISM CUBOID (square triangle sphere circle block)

13. ROSE PANSY DAISY TULIP (oak blossom thistle daffodil flower)

14. NOSE EYE LIP TEETH (face hand laugh cheek nerve)   / 4

Using Rules of English

Underline the correct word from the brackets to complete each sentence. Look at this example:

> I **(sit <u>sat</u> sitting)** very still while he painted my portrait.

Hint: Read the sentence out loud to yourself to help you choose the correct word.
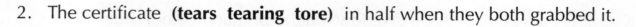

1. We **(works worked working)** really hard to win the dance competition.

2. The certificate **(tears tearing tore)** in half when they both grabbed it.

3. Milena was **(watching watch watches)** the TV when her brother came home.

4. The nurse is **(careful caring careless)** for his patients.

5. Dad **(kind kindly kindness)** offered to drive us home after the party.

/ 5

6. Tola is going to meet **(your yours you)** at the bus station.

7. Gus **(throw threw throws)** the cricket ball the furthest at last year's sports day.

8. The **(bunch team flock)** of sheep were in the middle of the road.

9. The sun was **(shine shone shining)** through the gap in the blinds.

10. Henry's trip to France was **(him his its)** first holiday abroad.

/ 5

11. Ava showed great **(brave bravely bravery)** by rescuing the cat from the tree.

12. Nena had **(run ran runs)** around the park in the morning before work.

13. Geoff whistled **(soft softly softness)** as he cleaned the car.

14. My sister **(has have had)** brown hair before she dyed it purple.

15. Beth **(lights lit light)** the candles in the sitting room yesterday.

/ 5

Choose a Word

Choose the correct word to complete each sentence below.

1. Shane cheered
   ☐ calmly
   ☐ sadly   when his team won the match.
   ☐ loudly

2. Marion was upset
   ☐ also
   ☐ because   her pet iguana was ill.
   ☐ due

3. Frédérique and Sandra are
   ☐ gone
   ☐ went   to paint a mural in the town hall.
   ☐ going

/ 3

4. There are fewer hours of
   ☐ daylight
   ☐ school   in the winter months.
   ☐ heating

5. The squirrel
   ☐ showed
   ☐ buried   ten acorns under the tree stump.
   ☐ climbed

6. Hannah
   ☐ explained
   ☐ wrote   the plot of the film to her sister.
   ☐ argued

/ 3

7. Lloyd's budgie was learning to
   ☐ speak
   ☐ recite   the alphabet.
   ☐ fly

8. We
   ☐ cut
   ☐ watered   the flowers nicely in the vase.
   ☐ arranged

9. Zoë was
   ☐ famished
   ☐ thirsty   because she hadn't eaten all morning.
   ☐ full

/ 3

 ✓ ✓ ✓

Section Three — Completing Passages

Choose a Word

Choose the correct words to complete each passage below.

During the Iron Age, Celtic people
1. ☐ fought
☐ lived
☐ swam
in roundhouses.

A roundhouse was a small house made from
2. ☐ plastic
☐ feeble
☐ natural
materials such

as wood and mud. These circular
3. ☐ buildings
☐ doors
☐ shops
had no windows, so they

were often quite dark inside.

/ 3

Karim packed his backpack
4. ☐ loudly
☐ hastily
☐ slowly
and rushed out of the house.

He
5. ☐ knocked
☐ prodded
☐ wiped
loudly at Anna's door, and she dashed out to meet him.

The two children raced to the park — they were excited
6. ☐ so
☐ when
☐ because
the fair

was coming to town today!

/ 3

Mount Vesuvius on Italy's west
7. ☐ land
☐ city
☐ coast
is the only active volcano in mainland

Europe. It last erupted in 1944, but it is best
8. ☐ known
☐ knowed
☐ know
for its eruption in

79 AD, when the cities of Herculaneum and Pompeii were
9. ☐ both
☐ only
☐ every
destroyed.

/ 3

Section Three — Completing Passages

21

Fill in Missing Letters

Fill in the missing letters to complete the words in the following sentences.

1. The audience were excited as they waited for the play to b☐g☐n .

2. Fiona was r☐s☐ing , so she forgot her purse.

3. The c☐☐ning fox sneaked into the chicken coop.

4. Tamwar provoked the bull, so it ch☐r☐ed towards him.

5. The doctor e☐ami☐ed my foot, but it wasn't broken.

/ 5

6. The whole family tr☐v☐ll☐d by train to get to the beach.

7. I sq☐e☐☐ed seven lemons to make some lemonade.

8. I d☐f☐n☐tely want to go to the museum tomorrow.

9. Raymond shaped the clay sk☐lfu☐☐y into a tall vase.

10. I couldn't find the inst☐☐c☐☐ons for the computer.

/ 5

11. Yesterday, I m☐☐☐☐ chocolate cakes for the village fete.

12. Sonia and Meryl had a dis☐☐☐sion about their trip to the zoo.

13. Ben hired a boat and r☐w☐☐ to the haunted island.

14. One day, I would like to write an adv☐nt☐☐e novel.

15. My su☐☐ca☐e split on the way to the airport.

/ 5

Section Three — Completing Passages

Fill in Missing Letters

Fill in the missing letters to complete the words in the following passages.

1. Pembroke Castle is a med☐☐val castle located in south west Wales.
   It was first built as a wooden motte and bailey castle,

2. but it was re☐la☐ed with a stone castle in the 12th century.

3. It is known for being the b☐rthpl☐☐e of King Henry VII.
   Today, the castle is owned by a charitable trust —

4. it is the largest pr☐v☐t☐ly owned castle in Wales.

5. Pembroke Castle is open to the public and hosts lots of events, such
   as falconry displays and storytelling, to ent☐☐t☐in visitors.

/ 5

6. In Greek m☐thol☐gy , Hermes was the son of Zeus
   and the second youngest of the Olympian gods.

7. Hermes wore winged sand☐☐s on his feet, which allowed him to fly.
   This meant he could travel between the gods and the mortals,

8. del☐v☐ring messages.

9. Hermes was believed to have invented ru☐☐ing races,

10. and he was known as the god of a☐☐let☐cs .

/ 5

11. There are many dif☐☐r☐nt species of whale.

12. The largest is the blue whale, which can reach a len☐☐☐ of 30 metres.
    However, the blue whale's brain is relatively small when compared to the sperm

13. whale, which has the largest brain of any animal that has ever e☐☐st☐d .

14. D☐sp☐te their great size, some whales, including the blue whale,

15. survive by eating tiny sea cr☐☐☐ures like plankton.

/ 5

Section Three — Completing Passages

Finding Hidden Facts

Read the information carefully, then use it to answer the question that follows. Write your answer on the line.

Hint: All the names are usually given in the first sentence — write these down as a list so you don't miss anyone.

1. Joe, Dave, Avanti, Caley and Marco are comparing their favourite sports.

   Joe, Dave and Marco like tennis. Caley likes badminton. Avanti and Dave like swimming. Everyone except Avanti likes rugby.

   Who likes the **most** sports? _____

2. Mohammed, Gavin, Lucy, Heather and Kat are comparing their favourite animals.

   Mohammed and Gavin like lions. Lucy and Mohammed like bats. Heather and Gavin like wolves. Everyone apart from Gavin likes snakes.

   Who likes the **most** animals? _____

3. Mr Davis, Mr Li, Mrs Pike, Mr College and Mr Williamson teach science.

   Everyone except Mr Li teaches Year 7. Mr College and Mr Davis teach Year 12 and Year 13. Mr Li teaches Year 9. Mrs Pike and Mr Davis teach Year 10.

   Who teaches the **most** classes? _____

4. Maisie, Lotte, Milly, Sanjay and Ceara are discussing TV programmes they like.

   Ceara and Sanjay like cartoons. Everyone likes comedy except Lotte. Maisie likes drama. Milly and Lotte like nature programmes.

   / 4

   Who likes the **fewest** types of programmes? _____

Multiple-Statement Questions — Logic

> Read the information carefully, then use it to answer the question that follows. Underline the correct answer.

1. Murphy, Geeta, Simon, Matthew and Hector are comparing their pocket money. Murphy and Hector both get £3. Geeta gets £4.
Simon gets half as much as Hector. Matthew gets twice as much as Geeta.
If these statements are true, only one of the sentences below **must** be true.
Which one?

   A   Geeta gets the most pocket money.
   B   Hector and Murphy get £4 each.
   C   Matthew gets less pocket money than Geeta.
   D   Simon gets the least amount of pocket money.

2. Ezra, Lettice, Sam and Greg are doing a spelling test. Sam scores full marks.
Greg and Lettice both get 11 wrong. Ezra scores 5 more than Lettice.
The test has 40 questions.
If these statements are true, only one of the sentences below **cannot** be true.
Which one?

   A   Sam scores 40.
   B   Greg scores 10 less than Sam.
   C   Ezra scores 34.
   D   They have half an hour to do the test.

3. Arundhati, Eddie, Gabby and Ailsa are measuring how tall they are.
Eddie is 10 cm taller than Ailsa. Ailsa and Arundhati are only 5 cm apart
in height. Arundhati is the shortest person. Gabby is shorter than Ailsa.
If these statements are true, only one of the sentences below **cannot** be true.
Which one?

   A   Ailsa is taller than Gabby.
   B   Arundhati is 110 cm tall.
   C   Ailsa is the second tallest.
   D   Gabby is 5 cm shorter than Eddie.

/ 3

Multiple-Statement Questions — Logic

Read the information carefully, then use it to answer the question that follows. Underline the correct answer.

4. Natasha, Edwin, Gary and Danvir are comparing how tall they are.
   Natasha is 7 cm taller than Danvir. Edwin is 160 cm tall.
   Danvir is 3 cm taller than Edwin. Gary is 3 cm shorter than Edwin.
   If these statements are true, only one of the sentences below **must** be true.
   Which one?

   A Danvir is 162 cm tall.
   B Natasha is the tallest.
   C Gary is not the shortest.
   D Edwin is 157 cm tall.

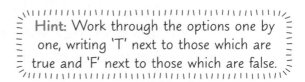

Hint: Work through the options one by one, writing 'T' next to those which are true and 'F' next to those which are false.

5. Rebecca, Matteo, Meg and Helen are all on a quiz team. The team get
   55 questions right. Rebecca and Matteo each answer the same number
   of questions correctly. Helen gets 5 more questions right than Meg.
   Meg answers 15 questions correctly.
   If these statements are true, only one of the sentences below **cannot** be true.
   Which one?

   A Helen gets the most questions right.
   B Helen answers more questions right than Meg.
   C Rebecca and Matteo both get 15 questions right.
   D Meg answers more questions right than Matteo.

6. Sofya, Kirsten, Rohan and Max are playing cards. Sofya and Max both win
   the same number of games. Kirsten wins 3 games. Rohan wins twice as many
   games as Kirsten. They play 13 games altogether.
   If these statements are true, only one of the sentences below **cannot** be true.
   Which one?

   A Rohan wins more games than Kirsten.
   B Sofya wins fewer games than Rohan.
   C Max wins 4 games.
   D Rohan wins the most games.

/ 3

Understanding the Language in the Text

> Read the passage below, and then answer the questions that follow.
> Underline the correct option for each question.

1   Ethan was only two streets away from home, but he still had to trudge
through Markdown Park, which he knew would be a squelching sponge.
He never enjoyed that part of the walk, but today, with the persistent rain and
wind, Ethan was even more reluctant than usual to hang around in the area.

5   Ethan's black terrier, Charlie, became a shadow as soon as he passed through
the gate into the gloomy park. Charlie growled quietly to himself: he didn't
seem to appreciate this evening's walk either.

As Ethan glanced at the sky, the charcoal-coloured clouds glared down at him
and the wind whipped cruelly at his exposed face.

1. The author says that the park was a "sponge" (line 2).
    This shows that the ground is:
    A soft and wet.   **B** dry and hard.   **C** clean and soft.

2. The author says that Ethan would have to "trudge" through the park (line 1).
    What does this tell you about his walk?
    A It would be quick.   **B** It would be relaxing. **C** It would be slow and difficult.

3. The author says that Ethan was "more reluctant than usual" to be in
    the park (line 4). Why do you think this is?
    A He is tired.   **B** The dog is growling.   **C** The weather is horrible.

4. The author says that Charlie was a "shadow" once they entered the park (line 5).
    This means that:
    A He followed Ethan. **B** He was hard to see.   **C** He was quiet.

5. The author says that the clouds "glared" at Ethan (line 8).
    This suggests that the clouds looked:
    A threatening.   **B** safe.   **C** comforting.

/ 5

Section Four — Comprehension

Mixed Comprehension Questions

Read the passage below, and then answer the questions that follow.

1   The Great Barrier Reef is situated off the north east coast of Australia. It is the largest coral reef system on the planet: it is around 3000 km long and covers an area of around 344 000 km². The vast size of the reef means that it is the only living thing on Earth that is visible from space.

5   The Great Barrier Reef is made up of more than 400 types of brightly coloured coral, and it is also home to over a thousand species of tropical fish, including yellow-faced angelfish, cardinalfish and tiger sharks. The area is also rich in other marine creatures, such as dolphins, rays and turtles.

One particularly interesting inhabitant is the giant clam. The giant clam
10   is the largest mollusc in the world (molluscs are creatures such as snails and mussels which have a soft body, often protected by a shell), and it can grow up to 1.2 metres across. Once this massive mollusc has chosen a spot on the reef, it remains fastened there for the rest of its life, which can be more than a hundred years! When its shell is open, each giant clam displays unique
15   colouring, with a vivid combination of bright blues, greens and browns.

Historically, the giant clam had a reputation for dining on passing swimmers. However, although they may eat passing plankton, no evidence has ever been found of a giant clam trapping a human, and the claims have been dismissed by scientists.

20   It is no surprise that the Great Barrier Reef is a popular tourist destination: the impressive underwater scenes attract many divers and snorkelers each year. The reef also attracts an array of sea birds which feed on the assortment of sea life. So, even above the surface, the area is blessed with a natural beauty that visitors adore.

Turn over for the questions

Mixed Comprehension Questions

Answer these questions about the text on page 27.
Circle the letter of the correct option for each question.

1. Which of the following does not describe the Great Barrier Reef?
   A Full of life
   B Colourful
   C Bare
   D Attractive

2. According to the text, which of these creatures can be found in the reef?
   A Clownfish
   B Rainbowfish
   C Mussels
   D Rays

3. Which of the following statements about the giant clam is not mentioned in the passage?
   A It is the largest mollusc in the world.
   B It feeds on fish.
   C It can live for over a hundred years.
   D It can grow up to 1.2 metres across.

4. Why have scientists dismissed the legends about the giant clams?
   A There is no evidence.
   B They want to keep the truth a secret.
   C The clams are beautiful.
   D The clams eat plankton.

5. Which of the following is not given as a reason for tourists visiting the Great Barrier Reef?
   A Diving opportunities
   B Natural beauty
   C Boat rides
   D Underwater scenes

/ 5

Mixed Comprehension Questions

Answer these questions about the text on page 27.
Circle the letter of the correct option for each question.

6. Which one of the following statements about the Great Barrier Reef
   is not mentioned in the passage?
   A It is the only living thing on the planet that can be seen from space.
   B It can be a dangerous place to swim.
   C It is home to a selection of different sea creatures.
   D It is a popular tourist destination.

7. According to the text, which of these animals are not molluscs?
   A Giant clams
   B Snails
   C Mussels
   D Turtles

8. Which of these words is closest in meaning to "particularly" (line 9)?
   A Strangely
   B Especially
   C Increasingly
   D Happily

9. Which of these words is closest in meaning to "unique" (line 14)?
   A Completely individual
   B Brightly patterned
   C Very shiny
   D Quite similar

10. Which of these phrases is closest in meaning
    to "dining on passing swimmers" (line 16)?
    A Taking food from passing swimmers
    B Chasing passing swimmers
    C Eating passing swimmers
    D Being eaten by passing swimmers

/ 5

Assessment Test 1

This book contains eight assessment tests, which get harder as you work through them to help you improve your Verbal Reasoning skills.

Allow 20 minutes to do this test and work as quickly and as carefully as you can.

If you want to attempt each test more than once, you will need to print **multiple-choice answer sheets** for these questions from our website — go to cgpbooks.co.uk/11plus/answer-sheets. If you'd prefer to answer the questions on the page, just follow the instructions in the question.

> Read this passage carefully and answer the questions that follow.

The Dinosaur Dipper

Sanjay and his dad had been waiting in the queue for the roller coaster for a long time. Bored, Sanjay tugged Dad's sleeve, "Are we nearly at the front?"

When the family had arrived at the theme park that morning they'd bought their tickets from a friendly lady who was dressed as a cavewoman. When they
5 walked through the gates of the theme park, the Dinosaur Dipper roller coaster was the first thing Sanjay had seen. It towered over the other rides, and its shiny green track looped high above the ground. Brightly-painted carriages zoomed along the tracks, and the passengers' excited cries echoed through the air.

"Can we go on that ride, Dad?" Sanjay had begged. "Please?"
10 "Be patient," Dad had replied. "We're going to take Maya on some smaller rides first." Maya was Sanjay's baby sister. She was only two, and she was running around and shouting excitedly because she was happy to be out of her pushchair.

Finally, Dad and Sanjay had left Maya and Mum at the café and made their way towards the Dinosaur Dipper, where they had queued for what seemed like hours.
15 All of a sudden, the queue in front of them surged forwards, and Sanjay saw an official-looking man helping people onto the ride. Sanjay watched a group of teenagers climb excitedly into the colourful carriages. They chatted and giggled as they strapped the safety belts on tightly. With a loud clang and a clatter, the carriages shot forward.
20 Sanjay felt butterflies in his stomach. Suddenly the ride seemed very high and very fast. He wasn't sure that it looked fun after all. Before Sanjay could say anything, Dad turned around and took his hand.

"Come on, it's our turn!" he said.

The crowd hurried forward and Sanjay was swept through the gate. Dad led
25 him towards a carriage with a huge grin on his face.

"This is going to be fun!"

Answer these questions about the text that you've just read.
Circle the letter that matches the correct answer.

1. Why did Sanjay not go on the Dinosaur Dipper straight away?

    A He was frightened.
    B Maya wanted to go on it later.
    C The queue was too long.
    D They took Maya on some other rides first.

2. Which of the following statements is not true?

    A Sanjay and his dad queued for the ride for a long time.
    B The teenagers ahead of Sanjay were nervous about the ride.
    C The ride made a loud sound as it set off.
    D The carriages moved very quickly when the ride set off.

3. Which of these two words describe the Dinosaur Dipper?

    A Bright and colourful
    B Tall and slow
    C Small and loopy
    D Fast and straight

4. What does Sanjay think about the roller coaster when he reaches the end
    of the queue?

    A He thinks it might break down.
    B He thinks it will be really boring.
    C He thinks it won't be very enjoyable.
    D He thinks it will be exciting.

5. Where is Maya while Sanjay and his dad are waiting to get on the Dinosaur Dipper?

    A On a smaller ride
    B With Mum in the café
    C In the queue with them
    D In the ticket office with Mum

(/ 5)

Carry on to the next question → →

Assessment Test 1

32

6. What is meant by the word "tugged" (line 2)?

   A Touched
   B Pulled
   C Pushed
   D Helped

7. What is meant by the word "chatted" (line 17)?

   A Whispered
   B Shouted
   C Talked
   D Laughed

8. What is meant by the phrase "Sanjay was swept through the gate" (line 24)?

   A Sanjay was pushed through the gate quickly.
   B Sanjay fell over before he reached the gate.
   C Sanjay walked calmly through the gate.
   D Sanjay jumped over the gate.

/ 3

Find the word that means the same, or nearly the same, as the word on the left.

Example: quiet   noise   shout   <u>silent</u>   fairly

9.	**tidy**	chore	neat	messy	broom
10.	**cold**	chilly	damp	warm	sneeze
11.	**tired**	yawn	hungry	attempted	sleepy
12.	**shy**	quiet	timid	unhappy	hidden
13.	**merry**	laugh	smile	jolly	excited
14.	**sprint**	waddle	jog	fling	dash
15.	**useful**	good	proper	helpful	hopeless
16.	**cuddle**	warm	sleep	hug	stroke

/ 8

Complete the word on the right so that it means the opposite, or nearly the opposite, of the word on the left.

Example: cry l a u g h

17. **happy** ☐ ☐ d

18. **naughty** ☐ o o ☐

19. **slow** ☐ a ☐ t

20. **stop** b e ☐ ☐ n

21. **play** ☐ o r ☐

22. **ignore** l ☐ s ☐ e n

23. **calm** s t r ☐ s ☐ ☐ d

24. **mixed** s e p ☐ r ☐ t e

/ 8

Four of the words in each list are linked. Underline the word that is **not** related.

Example: cat   dog   rabbit   <u>lion</u>   hamster

25. beans   carrots   cheese   onion   broccoli

26. gnome   elf   toadstool   fairy   leprechaun

27. shop   house   library   office   bank

28. leaf   stem   flower   bud   tree

29. tango   jig   boogie   saunter   jive

30. shark   crab   tuna   dolphin   whale

31. chair   cupboard   wardrobe   chest   cabinet

32. morning   tomorrow   evening   night   afternoon

/ 8

Carry on to the next question → →

Assessment Test 1

> Circle the letters next to the correct words to complete this passage.

33. **A** den
Jen and her friends decided to make a   **B** branch   in the
     C tree

34. **A** through
woods. First, they tied a rope   **B** between   two trees and put a plastic
     C inside

35. **A** collected
sheet over it. Next, they   **B** made   sticks and twigs to cover the
     C removed

36. **A** so
sheet   **B** whilst   it would blend into the trees. Finally, they put dried
     C and

37. **A** around
leaves   **B** by   the floor of the shelter to sit on.
     C on

38. **A** very
The hideout became Jen's   **B** favourite   meeting place, and
     C warm

39. **A** money
she decided to spend as much   **B** space   there as possible.
     C time

40. **A** enjoyed
Jen and her friends   **B** enjoy   playing games and exchanging
     C enjoying

secrets while hidden among the trees. Over time, the children found a

41. **A** expensive
collection of   **B** ugly   treasures from the forest to decorate their
     C interesting

42. **A** secret
     B visible   hideout.
     C wooden

/ 10

Total   / 42

End of Test

Assessment Test 1

Assessment Test 2

Allow 20 minutes to do this test and work as quickly and as carefully as you can.

You can print **multiple-choice answer sheets** for these questions from our website — go to cgpbooks.co.uk/11plus/answer-sheets. If you'd prefer to answer the questions on the page, just follow the instructions in the question.

> Read this passage carefully and answer the questions that follow.

Thank you letter

Dear Aunt Angela,

    I am writing to thank you for the present you gave me. I opened it on Christmas morning, but I must confess that I had peeled back a corner of the wrapping paper two days before. I had just got home from school and Mum was on the phone to Aunt

5 Glenda, so while her back was turned, I gave all my presents under the tree a squeeze. I could guess what most of them were, but I couldn't resist a quick peek at the one from you. When Mum saw that part of the paper had been ripped off she was furious and accused me of doing it, but I managed to convince her that Poppy had scratched it with her claws.

10   When I was finally allowed to open your present, I pretended to be surprised. I think I should have been given an award for my acting! I tore into the wrapping paper like a wild animal and gave a dramatic gasp when I opened it.

    I couldn't wait to play with your gift. I rushed into the garden, even though it was raining, and set up a goal post. I wanted to use Grandad's walking sticks, but they

15 wouldn't stand up by themselves, so I had to use one of Dad's garden gnomes and an upturned flowerpot instead. It was windy, so my first shot missed the goal by a mile and ended up near the shed, but my second shot hit the target fair and square! I ran around with my arms in the air to celebrate, just like the footballers on the television.

    Thanks again for the new football. It was definitely my favourite Christmas

20 present this year.

Love from,
Anita

Carry on to the next question → →

Answer these questions about the text that you've just read.
Circle the letter that matches the correct answer.

1.   What was the weather like when Anita went into the garden?

   A   It was windy and snowing.
   B   The wind was blowing and it was raining.
   C   It was raining and cold.
   D   It was cold and sunny.

2.   Why did Anita pretend to be surprised when she opened Aunt Angela's present?

   A   Anita didn't like the present.
   B   Poppy had already ripped off the wrapping paper.
   C   Aunt Angela bought Anita the same gift every year.
   D   Anita had already seen part of the present.

3.   Which of these words best describes the way that Anita opened
     Aunt Angela's present on Christmas Day?

   A   Quickly
   B   Carefully
   C   Slowly
   D   Curiously

4.   When did Anita try to guess what the presents were?

   A   Before school
   B   After dinner
   C   Late at night
   D   After school

5.   Where did Anita's first shot go?

   A   On the shed roof
   B   Near the shed
   C   In the next-door neighbour's garden
   D   In the goal

/ 5

6. What is meant by the word "ripped" (line 7)?

   A Smashed
   B Torn
   C Hurt
   D Stolen

7. What is meant by the word "furious" (line 7)?

   A Distracted
   B Sad
   C Disappointed
   D Angry

8. What is meant by the word "confess" (line 3)?

   A Admire
   B Agree
   C Behave
   D Admit

/ 3

Rearrange the words so that each sentence makes sense.
Underline the word which doesn't fit into the sentence.

Example: I dishes <u>bubble</u> the washed

---

9. our was homework hard tomorrow

10. my called so is Elvis cat

11. for I was school playground early

12. I to popcorn went the cinema

13. dinner stir we had pasta for

14. likes Andrea fishing really pond

15. Marco floor the climbing to climbed top

16. has door colour been the blue painted

/ 8

Carry on to the next question → →

Assessment Test 2

38

The words in capitals are related in some way. Underline the word
from the brackets that fits best with the words in capitals.

Example: JAZZ POP HIP-HOP RAP (beat <u>rock</u> music drums sing)

17. FLAN BROWNIE JELLY TRIFLE (pudding burger roast yoghurt sweet)

18. UNICORN DRAGON OGRE GIANT (dodo zebra man extinct mermaid)

19. ITALY FRANCE FIJI CANADA (Spain island holiday country nation)

20. TEACHER DOCTOR LAWYER EDITOR (student dentist work job adult)

21. CASHEW PECAN WALNUT ALMOND (log bush peanut leaf nut)

22. PEAR PLUM APPLE PEACH (bean fruit vegetable cherry grow)

/ 6

Find the word that means the opposite, or nearly the opposite,
of the word on the left.

Example: evil   friendly   cruel   <u>kind</u>   annoyed

23. **wide**	vast	small	narrow	delicate
24. **dark**	vacant	clear	vague	bright
25. **shout**	repeat	whisper	ask	giggle
26. **rapid**	dawdle	wait	unhurried	lazy
27. **polite**	funny	rude	selfish	friendly
28. **straight**	curved	crouch	flex	lean
29. **even**	smooth	odd	folded	balanced
30. **plain**	standard	blank	patterned	red
31. **lazy**	tired	busy	clever	hardworking
32. **alert**	sleepy	awake	bright	bored

/ 10

Assessment Test 2

Fill in the missing letters to complete the words in the following passage.

33.   It was a b e [ ] [ ] t i f u [ ] day for a walk in the

34. country, and Aaron couldn't w [ ] [ ] t.

35. Dad made a picnic and Mum p a [ ] [ ] [ ] d some jumpers and

waterproofs into a bag — just in case.

36.   The sun was shining and the crisp autumn l [ ] [ ] [ ] e s

37. crunched beneath their feet as the f [ ] m [ ] [ ] y walked through

the woodland to the lake. Mum and Dad were strolling along

38. a d [ ] [ ] [ ] i n g the scenery while Aaron ran ahead.

The lake finally came into view, and Aaron could see a group of

39. deer g [ ] [ ] [ ] i n g on the lush grass next to the water.

"Look, there are deer!" he called to his parents who had almost

40. c a [ ] [ ] [ ] t up with him.

The deer were startled by Aaron's cry, and ran into the forest.

41. However, as Aaron a p [ ] r [ ] [ ] c h e d the lake he saw that

one of the animals was still nearby. It was drinking from a puddle and

42. it hadn't n [ ] t [ ] [ ] e d the people walking towards it. When it

looked up, it froze for a second before running after the other deer.

/ 10

Total / 42

End of Test

Assessment Test 2

Assessment Test 3

Allow 20 minutes to do this test and work as quickly and as carefully as you can.

You can print **multiple-choice answer sheets** for these questions from our website — go to cgpbooks.co.uk/11plus/answer-sheets. If you'd prefer to answer the questions on the page, just follow the instructions in the question.

> Read this passage carefully and answer the questions that follow.

Roger's Records

"Dad?"

"What now?" Roger's father said wearily, without looking up from his newspaper. "Guess how old Robert Wadlow was when he could carry his father up the stairs."

"I've no idea," said Roger's father.

5   "Have a guess," Roger insisted.

"Twelve."

"Wrong! It says here that Robert Pershing Wadlow, the tallest man that ever lived, was nine years old. That's the same age as me!"

Mr Cherry had been forced to listen to many of these fascinating facts from

10 his son, but he only had himself to blame. It was his idea to buy Roger his first 'Book of World Records' three years ago and he had given his son the new edition every Christmas since then.

"Dad?"

"Yes, son."

15 "What do you think the record is for the furthest distance for spitting a watermelon seed?"

"Ten metres," said Mr Cherry, reading the same sentence in his newspaper for the fifth time.

"Wrong! It's actually seventy three metres!" yelled Roger triumphantly.

20 He loved it when his father got the answer wrong. He was a teacher but he didn't know his records. Roger searched for another killer question. He knew that he probably only had time for one more before his father's patience ran out. He started reading about the woman with the longest fingernails in the world.

"Dad?"

25 There was no reply. Roger looked across the living room at an outspread newspaper that seemed to have sprouted legs and feet. The feet were wearing tartan slippers, and coming from behind the newspaper was a sound like the breathing of a wounded warthog. Roger wondered if there was a record for the loudest snoring in the world!

Answer these questions about the text that you've just read.
Circle the letter that matches the correct answer.

1. How old is Roger?

    A Seven
    B Eight
    C Nine
    D Ten

2. What is Roger's father's job?

    A Journalist
    B Teacher
    C Policeman
    D Builder

3. Which word best describes how Roger's father feels about Roger's questions?

    A Confused
    B Proud
    C Furious
    D Uninterested

4. Which of these records is not mentioned in the story?

    A The World's furthest seed spit
    B The World's longest fingernails
    C The World's best-selling book
    D The World's loudest snore

5. Who does Roger's father blame for his son's endless questions?

    A Roger
    B Roger's teacher
    C Himself
    D Robert Wadlow

/ 5

Carry on to the next question → →

Assessment Test 3

6. What is meant by the word "fascinating" (line 9)?

   A Wrong
   B Boring
   C Correct
   D Interesting

7. What is meant by the word "sprouted" (line 26)?

   A Appeared
   B Grown
   C Walked
   D Eaten

8. What is meant by the phrase "killer question" (line 21)?

   A A question about death
   B A question about hunting
   C A difficult question
   D A final question

/ 3

Complete the word on the right so that it means the same, or nearly the same, as the word on the left.

Example: loose b a g g y

9. **fact** t _ _ t h

10. **rare** u _ c o _ m _ n

11. **blend** _ i x _ u _ e

12. **heavy** w e i _ _ t y

13. **wealthy** r _ _ h

14. **many** c o u _ t l _ s _

15. **narrow** s l _ _

16. **recall** r _ m _ m b _ r

/ 8

Circle the letters next to the correct words to complete this passage.

17. **A** went
On Friday, my class   **B** going   on a school trip to the zoo.
C visits

18. **A** was
I enjoyed watching all the animals. The lemurs   **B** seemed   very
C played

19. **A** being
intelligent and playful when I saw them   **B** having   fed, and
C been

20. **A** when
   B they   penguins made me laugh as they waddled around.
   C the

21. **A** Suddenly
   B Today   , my favourite part of the trip was when I saw
   C However

22. **A** bigger
an elephant. It was much   **B** enormous   than I expected.
C biggest

23. **A** towered
It   **B** flew   above us and stretched its long trunk out to
   C grew

24. **A** roots
reach leaves from the tallest   **B** trunks   of the trees. As we
C branches

25. **A** on
watched, it started playing in a large pond   **B** by   the fence.
C down

Then, the elephant began to spray water all over the crowd!

26. **A** complete
We were all   **B** completely   drenched, and the zookeeper
C completing

couldn't stop laughing!

/ 10

Carry on to the next question → →

Find the word that means the opposite, or nearly the opposite, of the word on the left.

Example: evil   friendly   cruel   <u>kind</u>   annoyed

27. **open**   begin   seal   busy   action

28. **strong**   hard   force   powerful   feeble

29. **subtle**   sharp   rude   direct   faint

30. **early**   clock   love   punctual   tardy

31. **false**   lie   fake   sincere   proven

32. **vital**   emergency   trivial   fine   serious

33. **safe**   money   risky   secure   prepared

34. **curious**   thoughtful   strange   funny   indifferent

35. **full**   tight   heavy   empty   light

36. **cool**   ice   scorching   melt   freeze

/ 10

Four of the words in each list are linked. Underline the word that is **not** related.

Example: cat   dog   rabbit   <u>lion</u>   hamster

37. meal   supper   breakfast   lunch   dinner

38. skip   bound   spring   chase   leap

39. cupcake   cookie   pasty   teacake   biscuit

40. ladybird   beetle   butterfly   wasp   wren

41. glass   cup   beaker   saucer   mug

42. basil   parsley   oak   thyme   mint

/ 6

Total   / 42

End of Test

Assessment Test 4

Allow 20 minutes to do this test and work as quickly and as carefully as you can.

You can print **multiple-choice answer sheets** for these questions from our website — go to cgpbooks.co.uk/11plus/answer-sheets. If you'd prefer to answer the questions on the page, just follow the instructions in the question.

Read this passage carefully and answer the questions that follow.

Castles

After the Normans invaded England in 1066, they immediately made their mark on the land by building castles all around the country. These castles were not just ordinary buildings, but were fortresses built to protect Norman soldiers from their enemies.

5   The earliest Norman castles were either made within an existing Roman fort or were motte and bailey castles. The word 'motte' means a natural or man-made mound and the word 'bailey' means an enclosure. The bailey was usually a yard area surrounded by a wall.

    These castles were built by local peasants and could be constructed quickly

10 and cheaply. First, they dug a deep, circular ditch, piling the earth from the ditch into the centre to form the motte. A wooden building called a 'keep' was built on top of the tall motte as a look-out point. As the keep was on high ground, it would have been difficult for enemy troops to attack it without being noticed. The deep ditch around the castle also helped to protect the castle from invaders.

15   The bailey was built next to the motte. There were many buildings within the bailey, including stables, storerooms, kitchens and living quarters. Many of the castle's workers lived and worked inside the bailey. The bailey was often surrounded by a palisade. This was a tall fence made using wooden stakes and was another important part of the castle's defence.

20   Although motte and bailey castles had advantages, their wooden frames caught fire easily. Therefore, over time, people started building castles out of stone to prevent them from burning down, and to ensure that they lasted longer.

Carry on to the next question → →

Answer these questions about the text that you've just read.
Circle the letter that matches the correct answer.

1. Which of the following is not given as a reason why the Normans built motte and bailey castles?

   A They were very big.
   B They were quick to build.
   C They were difficult to attack.
   D They were cheap to build.

2. According to the text, which of the following buildings was not in the bailey?

   A The stables
   B The school
   C Storerooms
   D Living quarters

3. Which of the following does not describe a 'motte'?

   A A Roman fort
   B A heap of earth
   C A natural mound
   D A high hill

4. According to the text, what was the purpose of the castle's 'keep'?

   A To attack from
   B To keep animals in
   C To store weapons in
   D To watch for enemies

5. According to the passage, why were later castles built out of stone instead of wood?

   A Stone was cheaper.
   B There was more stone available.
   C Wood could catch fire.
   D Stone was difficult to attack.

/ 5

6. What is meant by the word "prevent" (line 22)?

   A Help
   B Watch
   C Rescue
   D Stop

7. What is meant by the word "invaders" (line 14)?

   A Armies
   B Attackers
   C Friends
   D Defenders

8. What is meant by the phrase "made their mark on the land" (lines 1-2)?

   A Changed the way the land looked
   B Ruined the land
   C Wrote books about the country
   D Improved the country

/ 3

Complete the word on the right so that it means the opposite, or nearly the opposite, of the word on the left.

Example: cry   l a u g h

9. **disappointed**   g l ☐ ☐

10. **chatty**   s ☐ ☐ e n t

11. **slow**   r ☐ ☐ ☐ d

12. **witty**   h u m ☐ ☐ ☐ l e s s

13. **thankful**   u n g r ☐ ☐ ☐ f u l

14. **traditional**   ☐ o d ☐ r n

15. **juicy**   d ☐ ☐

16. **tasty**   b l ☐ n ☐

/ 8

Carry on to the next question → →

Assessment Test 4

Find the word that means the same, or nearly the same, as the word on the left.

Example: quiet   noise   shout   <u>silent</u>   fairly

17. **fair**   cruel   just   play   ugly

18. **pain**   fall   trip   medicine   ache

19. **stroll**   amble   run   race   jog

20. **dye**   glue   stain   paste   brush

21. **spin**   twirl   tip   circle   round

22. **slice**   open   portion   cake   start

23. **dark**   scary   bright   faint   dim

24. **gobble**   nibble   guzzle   taste   spill

25. **soothe**   argue   hurt   bandage   relieve

26. **startle**   shine   surprise   annoy   laugh

/ 10

Rearrange the words so that each sentence makes sense.
Underline the word which doesn't fit into the sentence.

Example: I dishes <u>bubble</u> the washed

27. friend Cassie are best is my

28. Bruno to likes flies on chase

29. in queasy felt tiger the

30. lasagne grows Mum the makes best

31. I the out poem pen copied

32. Fion of sang is singing tune out

/ 6

Fill in the missing letters to complete the words in the following passage.

"Can I have some grapes, please?" asked Mrs Rhency.

33. Mr Apple, the g r e [ ] n g r o [ ] [ ] r, took a bunch

from a shelf behind him.

34. He smiled at Mrs Rhency, who was his f a v [ ] [ ] r [ ] t e

customer.

35. She bought all her fruit and v e g [ ] t [ ] b l [ ] [ ] s from him

36. and she usually had a p [ ] [ ] c e of local gossip to tell him.

"Have you heard what Mr Gwynne has done now?"

37. Mrs Rhency couldn't hide her s a t [ ] s f a c t [ ] [ ] n

38. when the shopkeeper a d m [ ] t [ ] [ ] d that he had heard nothing.

"You know he lives on Yewtree Avenue? Where the houses are so

39. classy and e l [ ] g [ ] [ ] t ?"

Mr Apple smiled and nodded. He enjoyed the dramatic

40. a t m o s [ ] [ ] r e that Mrs Rhency created with even

the smallest item of news.

"Well, not anymore. He's painted his whole house

41. b r [ ] [ ] [ ] t orange! Can you imagine it?"

42. Mrs Rhency paid for her items and w a [ ] [ ] d to a friend as she

left the shop.

/ 10

Total   / 42

End of Test

Assessment Test 4

Assessment Test 5

Allow 20 minutes to do this test and work as quickly and as carefully as you can.

You can print **multiple-choice answer sheets** for these questions from our website — go to cgpbooks.co.uk/11plus/answer-sheets. If you'd prefer to answer the questions on the page, just follow the instructions in the question.

> Read this poem carefully and answer the questions that follow.

The Fieldmouse

Where the acorn tumbles down,
Where the ash tree sheds its berry,
With your fur so soft and brown,
With your eye so round and merry,
5   Scarcely moving the long grass,
Fieldmouse, I can see you pass.

Little thing, in what dark den,
Lie you all the winter sleeping?
Till warm weather comes again,
10 Then once more I see you peeping
Round about the tall tree roots,
Nibbling at their fallen fruits.

Fieldmouse, fieldmouse, do not go,
Where the farmer stacks his treasure,
15 Find the nut that falls below,
Eat the acorn at your pleasure,
But you must not steal the grain
He has stacked with so much pain.

Make your hole where mosses spring,
20 Underneath the tall oak's shadow,
Pretty, quiet harmless thing,
Play about the sunny meadow.
Keep away from corn and house,
None will harm you, little mouse.

by Cecil Frances Alexander

Answer these questions about the text that you've just read.
Circle the letter that matches the correct answer.

1. According to the poem, what should the fieldmouse not eat?

   A Acorns
   B Fruits
   C Berries
   D Corn

2. Which of these words best describes the fieldmouse?

   A Fat and happy
   B Pretty and gentle
   C Harmful and noisy
   D Hungry and tired

3. Which of these statements about the farmer is true?

   A He is very rich.
   B He stores grain.
   C He is sleepy.
   D He is merry.

4. Why does the fieldmouse "Scarcely" (line 5) move the grass?

   A Because the fieldmouse is so small
   B Because the fieldmouse's fur is so soft
   C Because the fieldmouse is so fast
   D Because the fieldmouse is sleeping

5. What is meant by the word "stacks" (line 14)?

   A Produces
   B Scatters
   C Counts
   D Heaps

6. What is meant by the word "sheds" (line 2)?

   A Huts
   B Grows
   C Drops
   D Shows

/ 6

Carry on to the next question → →

Assessment Test 5

Read the passage carefully, then use it to answer the questions that follow. Circle the letter that matches the correct answer.

Last summer, Calvin, Dre, Alesha and Mary all did sponsored walks for charity. They aimed to raise £500 between them. First, Calvin and Alesha walked 10 km. Next, Dre walked 1 km less than Alesha. Mary was the last person to walk because she was on holiday, but she walked twice as many kilometres as Dre. Mary raised half of the total sponsorship money. The total amount raised was £50 more than the group had intended.

7. Which of these statements **cannot** be true?

    A Dre walked 9 km.
    B Calvin walked fewer kilometres than Dre.
    C Calvin walked further than Dre.
    D Dre walked the shortest distance.

8. Which of these statements **must** be true?

    A Alesha walked the furthest.
    B The group raised £450.
    C Mary raised £275.
    D Mary raised £250.

/ 2

Four of the words in each list are linked. Underline the word that is **not** related.

    Example: cat   dog   rabbit   <u>lion</u>   hamster

9. boiling   freezing   scorching   blazing   sweltering

10. sticky   tacky   gluey   attached   syrupy

11. laugh   giggle   mutter   chuckle   snigger

12. write   scrawl   inscribe   print   draw

13. paper   cotton   silk   wool   felt

14. squirrel   mouse   crow   vole   rat

/ 6

Find the word that means the same, or nearly the same, as the word on the left.

Example: quiet   noise   shout   <u>silent</u>   fairly

15. **peculiar**   usual   new   bizarre   unexpected

16. **fragile**   soft   delicate   broken   smooth

17. **cry**   roar   sob   chortle   whisper

18. **refuse**   stop   disagree   admit   decline

19. **burst**   tear   balloon   pop   block

20. **private**   known   shared   secret   unique

21. **shake**   tip   roll   shiver   steady

22. **study**   examine   write   glance   library

/ 8

Find the word that means the opposite, or nearly the opposite, of the word on the left.

Example: evil   friendly   cruel   <u>kind</u>   annoyed

23. **bitter**   sour   sweet   tasty   strong

24. **guilty**   good   careful   fault   blameless

25. **argue**   agree   suffer   tolerate   calm

26. **weak**   bulky   strict   hard   powerful

27. **colourful**   bright   dark   busy   drab

28. **smug**   superior   modest   discontent   upset

29. **disruptive**   annoying   muddled   calming   noisy

30. **explore**   research   wonder   analyse   ignore

/ 8

Carry on to the next question → →

Assessment Test 5

> Circle the letters next to the correct words to complete this passage.

31. **A** for
Today we are going shopping **B** with decorations for my birthday party.
C buy

32. **A** However
B Hopefully we'll be able to buy some pirate flags
C Wherever

33. **A** also
B although I'm having a
C because

34. **A** Everyone
pirate party. **B** Friends is going to wear fancy dress. I've got an eyepatch and
C Guests

35. **A** Although
a sword, and I am going to paint a beard on my face too. **B** Even my dog,
C When

36. **A** worn
Max, is going to be **B** wear a headscarf!
C wearing

37. **A** booking
Mum has **B** booked a bouncy castle, and Dad is baking a cake
C book

38. **A** tasting
B shaped
C found

39. **A** lots
like a pirate ship. We're going to play **B** many of pirate games in the garden and
C some

eat jelly and ice cream.

40. **A** decided
I haven't **B** remembered who to invite yet, but
C checked

41. **A** the
B my best friends
C mine

Loreen, Ravi and Peter are definitely coming. They have

42. **A** before
B presently bought
C already

their outfits.

/ 12

Total / 42

End of Test

Assessment Test 5

Assessment Test 6

Allow 20 minutes to do this test and work as quickly and as carefully as you can.

You can print **multiple-choice answer sheets** for these questions from our website — go to cgpbooks.co.uk/11plus/answer-sheets. If you'd prefer to answer the questions on the page, just follow the instructions in the question.

> Read this passage carefully and answer the questions that follow.

Aunt Florence

Some people thought that Ruby's aunt was slightly odd, others said she was away with the fairies. Aunt Florence wore multi-coloured clothes, dyed her long hair as red as a post box and had peculiar habits (singing in the supermarket was a particularly embarrassing one). Ruby's older brother Alfie said that she got confused
5 about what was real and what was imaginary. Alfie said that this was because Aunt Florence was a writer, but Ruby believed everything she said.

The day before yesterday, Aunt Flo had given Ruby a key: a thick, rusty, unimpressive-looking key. It looked as if it had not turned a lock in a long, long time, Ruby thought. Lowering her voice, Aunt Flo had told Ruby that it opened a
10 secret door in the attic of Grandpa's house; a door which led to another world. This was an enchanted world of magical people and strange creatures; a world Flo herself had visited when she was Ruby's age.

"The door will only reveal itself," Ruby's aunt had whispered, "if the person holding the key believes that the magical door exists."
15 Now Ruby was standing alone in the dusty, disorderly, dimly-lit attic, holding the key. Grandpa's old train set was laid out in the middle of the floor, as if he had just been playing with it. Around the train set were boxes and books and old photo albums, all piled high. But there was no sign of a door.

"Where are you? I know you are here somewhere," Ruby said quietly as she
20 searched the room.

Suddenly, the walls began to shake. Mortar crumbled from between the bricks and spiders scurried away from their cobwebs. Ruby stared in astonishment as a wonky, wooden door slowly appeared in the wall.

Carry on to the next question → →

Answer these questions about the text that you've just read.
Circle the letter that matches the correct answer.

1. Which statement about Aunt Florence is not true?

    A She has a niece and a nephew.
    B She has strange habits.
    C She has short hair.
    D She sings in public.

2. When did Aunt Florence give Ruby the key?

    A Two days ago
    B One week ago
    C One day ago
    D Three days ago

3. How did Aunt Florence speak to Ruby when she gave her the key?

    A Quickly
    B Loudly
    C Quietly
    D Jokingly

4. Which of the following statements about the attic is not true?

    A It was dark.
    B It was dirty.
    C It was in Aunt Florence's house.
    D It was filled with boxes and other old things.

5. Why did Ruby look at the door "in astonishment" (line 22)?

    A The door was made of gold.
    B The door was covered in cobwebs.
    C The door was breaking apart.
    D The door had appeared from nowhere.

6. What is meant by the word "imaginary" (line 5)?

    A Factual
    B Dishonest
    C Honest
    D Invented

/ 6

7. What is meant by the word "reveal" (line 13)?

   A Unlock
   B Show
   C Open
   D Hide

8. What is meant by the phrase "away with the fairies" (line 2)?

   A Difficult to find
   B Daydreaming
   C In the garden
   D Playing games

(/ 2)

Complete the word on the right so that it means the same, or nearly the same, as the word on the left.

Example: loose b a g g y

9. **funny** e n t ☐ r t ☐ ☐ n i n g

10. **find** d ☐ s c o ☐ ☐ r

11. **fall** t u m ☐ ☐ ☐

12. **prance** l ☐ ☐ p

13. **annoying** i r ☐ ☐ t a t ☐ n g

14. **sprinkle** s c ☐ t t ☐ ☐

15. **sparkle** s ☐ i m ☐ ☐ r

16. **absent** m ☐ ☐ s i n ☐

17. **circle** ☐ i ☐ g

18. **flurry** g ☐ s t

(/ 10)

Carry on to the next question → →

Complete the word on the right so that it means the opposite, or nearly the opposite, of the word on the left.

Example: cry l a u g h

19. **close** d i □ □ n t

20. **expose** c □ n c □ □ l

21. **tame** w □ □ d

22. **chubby** s □ r a □ n y

23. **catch** f □ e □

24. **complex** □ i □ p □ e

25. **attractive** r e p □ l □ i v □

26. **wrong** c o □ □ □ c t

27. **obvious** h □ d d □ □

28. **childish** m a t □ □ □

/ 10

The words in capitals are related in some way. Underline the word from the brackets that fits best with the words in capitals.

Example: JAZZ POP HIP-HOP RAP (beat <u>rock</u> music drums sing)

29. TRIANGLE CYMBAL TAMBOURINE GONG
   (sound music instrument drums flute)

30. LAMB FOAL CALF KID
   (horse tractor cow piglet farm)

31. MONDAY FRIDAY WEDNESDAY TUESDAY
   (Saturday weekend morning Thursday Sunday)

32. CABIN BUNGALOW CARAVAN MANSION
   (cottage patio building grand home)

/ 4

Fill in the missing letters to complete the words in the following passage.

Yesterday, I had to go to the dentist for a check-up.

33. I wasn't looking [f][ ][r][w][ ][ ][d] to it.

34. My sister kept [t][ ][ ][s][i][n][ ] me, saying that it would

35. be horrible and very [p][ ][ ][n][f][u][ ].

36. I had brushed my [t][ ][ ][ ][h] extra carefully all week

37. to [p][r][ ][p][ ][r][ ] myself for the dreadful

38. [e][x][p][e][r][ ][ ][n][ ][e].

39. However, when I got there, the dentist [l][ ][ ][ ][k][e][ ]

   at my teeth and said that they were the best teeth that she'd

40. seen all week. Then she gave me a [s][ ][ ][i][c][k][ ][ ] of a

41. rabbit with [s][p][ ][r][k][ ][ ][n][g] teeth, and told me to

   keep up the good work. I couldn't wait to get home to show

42. my sister my [s][p][e][ ][ ][ ][ ][l] sticker and my dazzling smile.

/ 10

Total | / 42

End of Test

Assessment Test 6

Assessment Test 7

Allow 20 minutes to do this test and work as quickly and as carefully as you can.

You can print **multiple-choice answer sheets** for these questions from our website — go to cgpbooks.co.uk/11plus/answer-sheets. If you'd prefer to answer the questions on the page, just follow the instructions in the question.

> Read this passage carefully and answer the questions that follow.

The Ancient Olympics

The first Olympic Games were held nearly 3000 years ago in Greece. They were held to honour Zeus, king of the gods, and took place in a stadium in the valley of Olympia. The Olympics were celebrated every four years as a sporting and religious festival and could draw large crowds of up to 40 000 people.

5   The games started with worship in a great temple near the stadium. A specially carved statue of Zeus made from gold and ivory, six times bigger than the average man, was the focus of the celebrations. The competitors had to swear an oath to Zeus that they had trained for ten months to prepare for the events.

     After the ceremony, the games began. One of the most demanding events was

10 the pentathlon. This consisted of five activities: running, throwing the javelin (a spear), throwing a discus (a metal disc), wrestling and long jump, and required great strength and determination from the athletes. The final race of the games was the challenging hoplite race, where the runners had to wear armour and carry shields. The winner of each Olympic event was presented with a special crown made from

15 olive leaves.

     The Olympic Games were held for over a thousand years until they were banned by the Romans. They were restarted as the modern Olympics in 1896. The modern games include many of the same events as the ancient games, such as races and the long jump, as well as new activities like swimming and fencing. Although the

20 Olympics are now held all over the world, they are still celebrated every four years.

Answer these questions about the text that you've just read.
Circle the letter that matches the correct answer.

1. Where did the sporting events of the Ancient Olympics take place?

   A In a stadium in Olympia
   B In a different district every four years
   C In stadiums all over the world
   D In the mountains of Greece

2. What did the winners receive?

   A Gold and ivory
   B A specially carved statue of Zeus
   C A medal
   D A crown made of leaves

3. According to the text, which of the following statements about Zeus is not true?

   A The games ended with everybody worshipping Zeus.
   B The statue of Zeus was taller than a man.
   C The statue of Zeus was made from gold and ivory.
   D The Olympic Games were held to honour Zeus.

4. Why was the hoplite race difficult?

   A It was the final race of the games.
   B It was the last event in the pentathlon.
   C The runners had to run long distances.
   D The runners had to wear heavy armour.

5. Which of the following does not describe the Ancient Olympic Games?

   A They were banned by the Romans.
   B They could draw large crowds of thousands of people.
   C They were dedicated to the king of the Greeks.
   D They were a religious festival.

/ 5

Carry on to the next question → →

6. What does the phrase "to honour Zeus" (line 2) mean?

    A To crown Zeus
    B To visit Zeus
    C To vote for Zeus
    D To praise Zeus

7. What does the word "oath" (line 7) mean?

    A Prayer
    B Promise
    C Treasure
    D Belief

8. What does the word "strength" (line 12) mean?

    A Power
    B Muscles
    C Training
    D Skill

/ 3

Find the word that means the opposite, or nearly the opposite, of the word on the left.

Example: evil   friendly   cruel   <u>kind</u>   annoyed

---

9. **curly**	straight	frizzy	tousled	neat
10. **current**	new	contemporary	historic	wave
11. **dawdle**	rush	walk	relax	loiter
12. **manic**	crazy	berserk	happy	calm
13. **empty**	hollow	congested	stuck	tired
14. **puzzling**	confusing	complicated	interesting	straightforward
15. **expensive**	costly	reasonable	overpriced	lavish
16. **sociable**	friendly	busy	unfriendly	talkative
17. **ordinary**	irrational	eccentric	routine	intelligent
18. **return**	arrive	travel	departure	turn

/ 10

Complete the word on the right so that it that means the same, or nearly the same, as the word on the left.

Example: loose [b][a][g][g][y]

19. **energetic** [a][ ][t][ ][v][ ]

20. **silly** [f][o][ ][l][i][ ][h]

21. **precise** [s][p][ ][c][i][ ][ ][c]

22. **bare** [e][ ][p][ ][ ]

23. **error** [ ][i][s][ ][a][ ][e]

24. **match** [g][ ][ ][e]

25. **merge** [c][ ][m][b][ ][n][e]

26. **neat** [o][r][ ][e][ ][ ][y]

/ 8

Four of the words in each list are linked. Underline the word that is **not** related.

Example: cat   dog   rabbit   <u>lion</u>   hamster

27. van   bike   car   lorry   campervan

28. piano   flute   oboe   saxophone   trombone

29. coat   cardigan   anorak   jacket   mackintosh

30. crayon   pencil   chalk   rubber   pen

31. like   prefer   admire   adore   disapprove

32. noun   verb   comma   adverb   adjective

/ 6

Carry on to the next question → →

Assessment Test 7

64

Circle the letters next to the correct words to complete this passage.

The school netball team are celebrating
33. **A** some
B lots
C many
great news. They have

34. **A** beaten
B won
C lifted
the finals of the national championships! At first, they made us all

35. **A** believe
B remember
C know
that they had lost. We knew they were

36. **A** pretending
B joking
C tricking
us

though, because they couldn't stop smiling!

They said that the final match of the
37. **A** game
B tournament
C netball
had been a real challenge.

The runners-up
38. **A** was
B were
C weren't
very tough to beat — they
39. **A** has
B have
C had
won the

championships last year. The coach told us that the
40. **A** audience
B players
C team
was dazzled by

the skill
41. **A** demonstrated
B played
C managed
by both teams, and nobody could tell who would win

until the
42. **A** almost
B very
C second
last minute.

/ 10

Total   / 42

End of Test

Assessment Test 7

Assessment Test 8

Allow 20 minutes to do this test and work as quickly and as carefully as you can.

You can print **multiple-choice answer sheets** for these questions from our website — go to cgpbooks.co.uk/11plus/answer-sheets. If you'd prefer to answer the questions on the page, just follow the instructions in the question.

> Read this poem carefully and answer the questions that follow.

Winter Time

Late lies the wintry sun a-bed,
A frosty, fiery sleepy-head;
Blinks but an hour or two; and then,
A blood-red orange, sets again.

5   Before the stars have left the skies,
At morning in the dark I rise;
And shivering in my nakedness,
By the cold candle, bathe and dress.

Close by the jolly fire I sit
10 To warm my frozen bones a bit;
Or with a reindeer-sled, explore
The colder countries round the door.

When to go out, my nurse doth wrap
Me in my comforter* and cap;
15 The cold wind burns my face, and blows
Its frosty pepper up my nose.

Black are my steps on silver sod**;
Thick blows my frosty breath abroad;
And tree and house, and hill and lake,
20 Are frosted like a wedding-cake.

by Robert Louis Stevenson

*comforter — *a scarf*
**sod — *soil*

Carry on to the next question → →

Answer these questions about the text that you've just read.
Circle the letter that matches the correct answer.

1. Which of these things is not mentioned in the poem?

   A Sun
   B Fire
   C Stars
   D Moon

2. Why does the child dress by candlelight?

   A The child is cold.
   B It is night time.
   C It is dark in the morning.
   D The child is scared of the dark.

3. Which of these events happens last in the poem?

   A The child goes outside.
   B The child shivers in the candlelight.
   C The child washes and gets dressed.
   D The child gets warm by the fire.

4. In line 17, the child notices that the frost is melted by:

   A the rain.
   B the fire.
   C the reindeer sled.
   D footsteps.

5. What does the word "explore" (line 11) mean?

   A Move from
   B Travel around
   C Arrive
   D Depart from

6. What does the phrase "Late lies the wintry sun a-bed" (line 1) mean?

   A The sun doesn't tell the truth.
   B The sun is late to rise.
   C The sun is shining.
   D It's time to get out of bed.

/ 6

Find the word that means the same, or nearly the same, as the word on the left.

Example: quiet   noise   shout   <u>silent</u>   fairly

7. **confined**   enclosed   free   locked   closed
8. **strange**   interesting   abnormal   normal   expected
9. **float**   sink   ship   drift   paddle
10. **trim**   cut   design   expand   amplify
11. **skim**   analyse   study   scan   read
12. **bossy**   inferior   preferable   superior   overbearing
13. **emotional**   calm   upset   discreet   harsh
14. **tired**   weary   invigorated   slumbering   exhaust

/ 8

Complete the word on the right so that it means the opposite, or nearly the opposite, of the word on the left.

Example: cry   l a u g h

15. **surprising**   p r _ d i c t _ b l _
16. **inadequate**   a c _ _ p t _ b l e
17. **lovely**   h _ r r _ b _ _
18. **exciting**   h _ m d r _ m
19. **spicy**   _ i l _
20. **sweet**   s _ _ r
21. **immature**   r _ s p _ n s _ b l e
22. **wise**   i _ n o r _ _ t

/ 8

Carry on to the next question → →

Assessment Test 8

Read the passage carefully, then use it to answer the questions that follow. Circle the letter that matches the correct answer.

Emily had been looking forward to the baking class all week, but she was in such a rush that she was halfway there before she realised that she had forgotten her six eggs. She had to go back for the eggs, which made her 15 minutes late. Helen and Bryn arrived 30 minutes before Jonny, and had a dozen eggs between them.

When Usamah and Jonny finally arrived at 8.00, they had brought four eggs each. However, because the class started at 7.30, they were too late to bake the cake they had planned. They decided to help Emily decorate her cake instead.

23. Which of these statements must be true?

    A   Emily arrived before Helen and Bryn.
    B   Helen and Bryn arrived on time for the class.
    C   Bryn and Usamah arrived together.
    D   Jonny arrived first.

24. Which of these statements cannot be true?

    A   Bryn had 8 eggs.
    B   Bryn had more eggs than Helen.
    C   Helen had more eggs than Emily.
    D   The friends had 20 eggs in total.

/ 2

Rearrange the words so that each sentence makes sense. Underline the word which doesn't fit into the sentence.

Example: I dishes <u>bubble</u> the washed

25. shout the Jack from giant hid

26. lamb Sabrina held tightly the stroke

27. I stars saw sky shooting three

28. drove Ashok blue a early car

29. the Pip could read shelf reach not

30. danced the everybody song party at

/ 6

Assessment Test 8

Fill in the missing letters to complete the words in the following passage.

31.　　　　I b [ ] [ ] g [ ] t a unicycle from a junk shop last week.

32. It was a b [ ] r g [ ] [ ] n because the shopkeeper just wanted it

　　to go to a good home.

33. I [ ] r o m [ ] [ ] e d that I would take good care of it,

34. and went straight to the park to [ ] r a [ ] t [ ] s e.

35.　　　　Riding a unicycle requires an excellent sense of b [ ] l [ ] n c e.

36. At first, I couldn't even stay u [ ] r i [ ] [ ] t for two seconds,

37. but I kept trying until my b r [ ] t [ ] e r called me in for dinner.

　　　　The park is right next door to our house, so I took my unicycle there

38. every day for a week. For the first c o [ ] [ ] l [ ] of days I kept falling

39. off, so I had a few cuts and b r [ ] [ ] s e [ ], but now I can ride with

　　my eyes closed.

40.　　　　All of my friends are i m [ ] r e s [ ] e [ ] by my new skill —

41. one of them even said that I was good e n o [ ] [ ] [ ] to be a

42. professional unicyclist. However, I think I'll learn to j u [ ] [ ] l [ ]

/ 12

　　at the same time before I join the circus!

Total　　/ 42

End of Test

Assessment Test 8

Glossary

adjective	A word that <u>describes</u> a <u>noun</u>, e.g. '<u>beautiful</u> morning', '<u>frosty</u> lawn'.
adverb	A word that <u>describes</u> a <u>verb</u>, which often ends with the <u>suffix</u> '<u>-ly</u>', e.g. 'She laughed <u>happily</u>.', 'He ran <u>quickly</u>.'
antonym	A word that has the <u>opposite meaning</u> to another, e.g. an antonym of 'good' is 'bad'.
conjunction	A word that <u>joins</u> two clauses, e.g. '<u>and</u>', '<u>but</u>'.
consonants	The <u>21 letters</u> of the alphabet that <u>aren't vowels</u>.
fiction	Text that has been <u>made up</u> by the author, usually about <u>imaginary people</u> and <u>events</u>.
homophones	Words that <u>sound the same</u>, but mean different things, e.g. '<u>hair</u>' and '<u>hare</u>'.
imagery	Language that creates a <u>vivid picture</u> in the reader's mind.
multiple choice	A type of <u>11+ question</u> that gives you <u>answers</u> to choose from.
non-fiction	Text that is about <u>facts</u> and <u>real people</u> and <u>events</u>.
noun	A word that <u>names</u> something, e.g. '<u>Paul</u>', '<u>cat</u>', '<u>fear</u>', '<u>love</u>'.
prefix	Letters that can be put <u>in front</u> of a word to <u>change its meaning</u>, e.g. '<u>un-</u>' can be added to '<u>lock</u>' to make '<u>unlock</u>'.
pronoun	Words that can be used <u>instead</u> of <u>nouns</u>, e.g. '<u>I</u>', '<u>you</u>', '<u>he</u>', '<u>it</u>'.
suffix	Letters that can be put <u>after</u> a word to <u>change its meaning</u>, e.g. '<u>-er</u>' can be added to the end of '<u>play</u>' to make '<u>player</u>'.
synonym	A word with a <u>similar meaning</u> to another word, e.g. '<u>big</u>' is a synonym of '<u>huge</u>'.
verb	An <u>action</u> or <u>doing</u> word, e.g. '<u>run</u>', '<u>went</u>', '<u>think</u>', or a <u>being</u> word, e.g. '<u>is</u>'.
vowels	The letters '<u>a</u>', '<u>e</u>', '<u>i</u>', '<u>o</u>' and '<u>u</u>'.

V4QDE2